Other titles in this series:
The Victim's Guide to Air Travel
The Victim's Guide to Christmas
The Victim's Guide to the Dentist
The Victim's Guide to the Doctor
The Victim's Guide to Middle Age

Published simultaneously in 1994 by Exley Publications in Great
Britain, and Exley Giftbooks in the USA.

Cartoons copyright © Roland Fiddy, 1994
Copyright © Exley Publications Ltd.

ISBN 1-85015-503-8

Printed in Spain by Grafo, S.A. Bilbao.

Exley Publications Ltd, 16 Chalk Hill, Watford, Herts WD1 4BN, UK.
Exley Giftbooks, 232 Madison Avenue, Suite 1206, New York,
NY 10016, USA.

THE VICTIM'S GUIDE TO ...

The Baby

EXLEY

NEW YORK · WATFORD, UK

FATHERS WHO ARE PRESENT AT THE BIRTH FIND IT AN
UNFORGETTABLE EXPERIENCE......

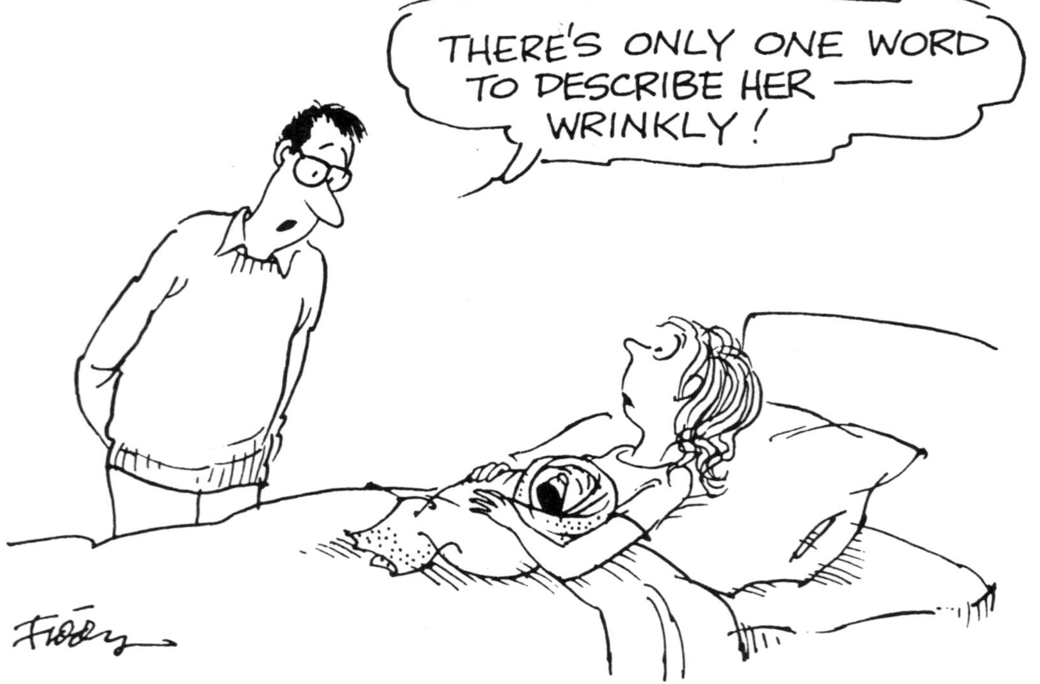
THERE'S ONLY ONE WORD TO DESCRIBE HER — WRINKLY!
Fiddy

A GOOD PARENT SHOULD ALWAYS TRY TO
SEE THINGS FROM THE CHILD'S POINT OF VIEW ...

BABY'S EYE VIEW

DADDY

DOTING RELATIVES

NIGHT TIME

MOTHER

STAIRS

DOGGY

PUSSY..................CAT!!

COLIC ALTHOUGH IT IS DISTRESSING, COLIC IS NOT DANGEROUS. TRY NOT TO BECOME STRESSED, AS THIS COULD AFFECT THE BABY.

NEW PARENTS SPEND A LOT OF TIME TRYING TO MAKE ENDS MEET.....

...AND SO DOES THE BABY.

*"MY MOTHER DOESN'T UNDERSTAND ME"

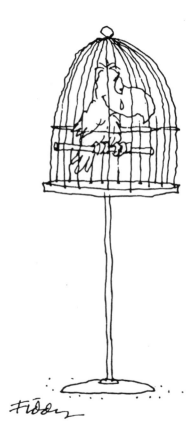

①

②

③

④

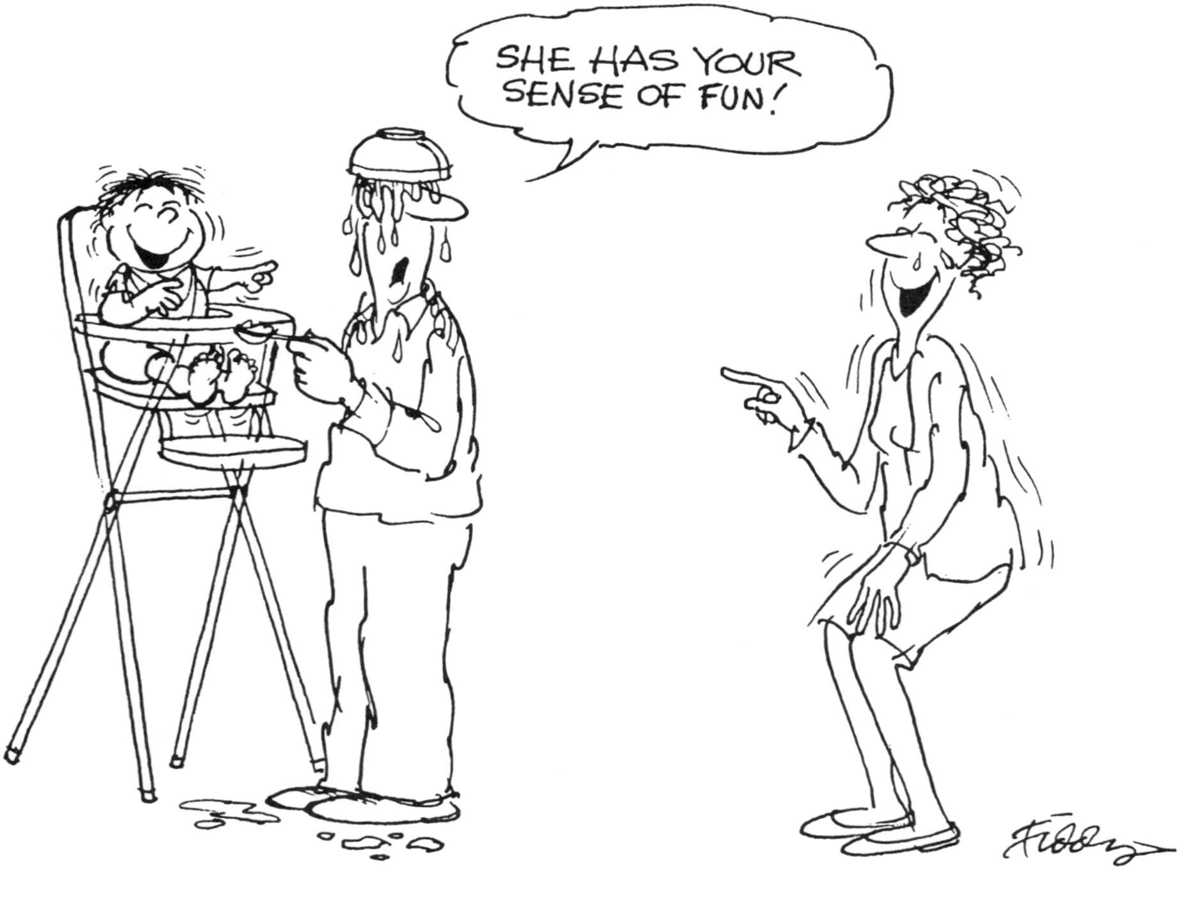
SHE HAS YOUR SENSE OF FUN!

⑤　⑥　⑦　⑧

⑩

①

②

③

④

⑤

⑥

① MUD....

② ... MUD....

③

④

.... GLORIOUS ....

... MUD ....

⑤

⑥

①

②

③

Books in the "Victim's Guide" series
($4.99 £2.99 paperback)

Award-winning cartoonist Roland Fiddy sees the funny side of life's phobias, nightmares and catastrophes.

The Victim's Guide to Air Travel
The Victim's Guide to the Baby
The Victim's Guide to Christmas
The Victim's Guide to the Dentist
The Victim's Guide to the Doctor
The Victim's Guide to Middle Age

The "Fanatic's" series
($4.99 £2.99)

The **Fanatic's Guides** are perfect presents for everyone with a hobby that has got out of hand. Eighty pages of hilarious black and white cartoons by Roland Fiddy.

The Fanatic's Guide to the Bed
The Fanatic's Guide to Cats
The Fanatic's Guide to Computers
The Fanatic's Guide to Dads
The Fanatic's Guide to Diets
The Fanatic's Guide to Dogs
The Fanatic's Guide to Husbands
The Fanatic's Guide to Money
The Fanatic's Guide to Sex
The Fanatic's Guide to Skiing

Books in the "Crazy World" series
($4.99 £2.99 paperback)

The Crazy World of Aerobics (Bill Stott)
The Crazy World of Cats (Bill Stott)
The Crazy World of Cricket (Bill Stott)
The Crazy World of Gardening (Bill Stott)
The Crazy World of Golf (Mike Scott)
The Crazy World of the Greens (Barry Knowles)
The Crazy World of the Handyman (Bill Stott)
The Crazy World of Hospitals (Bill Stott)
The Crazy World of Housework (Bill Stott)
The Crazy World of the Learner Driver (Bill Stott)
The Crazy World of Love (Roland Fiddy)
The Crazy World of Marriage (Bill Stott)
The Crazy World of Rugby (Bill Stott)
The Crazy World of Sailing (Peter Rigby)
The Crazy World of Sex (David Pye)
The Crazy World of Soccer (Bill Stott)

Books in the "Mini Joke Book" series
($6.99 £3.99 hardback)

These attractive 64 page mini joke books are illustrated throughout by Bill Stott.

A Binge of Diet Jokes
A Bouquet of Wedding Jokes
A Feast of After Dinner Jokes
A Knockout of Sports Jokes
A Portfolio of Business Jokes
A Round of Golf Jokes
A Romp of Naughty Jokes
A Spread of Over-40s Jokes
A Tankful of Motoring Jokes

Great Britain: Order these super books from your local bookseller or From Exley Publications Ltd, 16 Chalk Hill, Watford, Herts WDl 4BN. Please send £1.30 to cover post and packaging on 1 book, £2.60 on 2 or more books.)